LAWSON

WE HOPE YOU ENJOY
PLAYING THESE SONGS AS
MUCH AS WE DO EVERYNIGHT
OUT ON STAGE.

LAWSON

STANDING IN THE DARK

Words & Music by David Morgan, Andrew Brown,
Ki Fitzgerald & Ryan Fletcher

1. Sit-ting here wide a-wake,— think-in' a-bout— when I— last saw— you. I

know I'm not one to chase._____ I've nev-er want-ed noth-in' more,_____
as he turns down the lights_____ I'm feel-ing pa-ra - lysed.____

but as I walk up to your door..._____
And as he looks in-to her eyes..._____ }
I'm

stand-ing in the dark, she's danc-ing on the ta - ble. Look-ing through the glass, she's

some-one els-e's an - gel. It may sound stu-pid that I want-ed you back,_ but I

7

GONE

Words & Music by Andrew Brown

TAKING OVER ME

Words & Music by John Shanks & Andrew Brown

15

EVERYWHERE YOU GO

Words & Music by Christopher Young, Andrew Brown,
Talay Riley & Ki Fitzgerald

23

WHEN SHE WAS MINE

Words & Music by Andy Brown, Ki Fitzgerald,
Paddy Dalton & Mark Blackwell

26

28

Down on my knees, got to see her. Got to see her. Got-ta see her. Tried to for-get but I need her. But I need her. But I need her.

Repeat ad lib.

need her. When she___ was mine.___

WATERFALL

Words & Music by Andrew Brown, Jez Ashurst
& Emma Rohan

MAKE IT HAPPEN

Words & Music by Andrew Brown & Jez Ashurst

love you got-ta make it hap - pen, it hap - pen. Ooh.____

Whoa,_ oh.____ You got-ta make it hap-

38

LEARN TO LOVE AGAIN

Words & Music by Carl Falk, Rami Yacoub, Andrew Brown,
Eric Turner, Michel Zitron & Joakim Berg

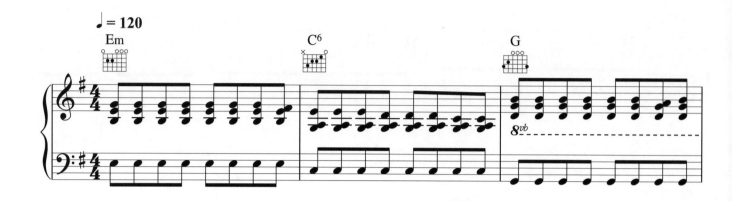

1. There's a place we know, what's cold

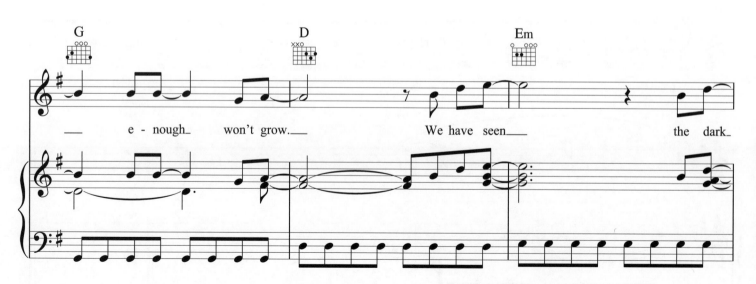

e - nough won't grow. We have seen the dark

YOU'LL NEVER KNOW

Words & Music by Andrew Brown & Jez Ashurst

youʼll nev-er know_ that I think_ a-bout you ev-er-y day._

1.

2, 3.

Youʼll nev-er know_ these tears_ Iʼve cried,_ that Iʼm sleep-ing on_ your side._ And if youʼre think-ing of me_

I donʼt, I donʼt know. Youʼll nev-er know_ Iʼm up_ all night. Youʼre still the best_ thing in_ my life._

STOLEN

Words & Music by Andrew Brown, Ki Fitzgerald,
Paddy Dalton & Blackwell Duck

1. Lights out, and it's___ cold now. And there's___ noth-ing but an
2. Word's out, I won't___ stand down. Got your___ face up now on

emp-ty room___ in front of me.___ I'm___ wiped out and the___ line's down. And there's___
ev-'ry wall___ of ev-'ry street. I___ re-trace ev-'ry___ step I made back to___

51

I took it all for grant-ed when I should-'ve took your hand.
You were the on-ly thing I
need-ed but I could-n't see.
Just look a-round, there's noth-ing left of me.
Ev-'ry-thing's sto-
len, sto-len. Yeah.__
Ev-'ry-thing's sto-len, sto-len. Yeah.__

I knew you had__ to leave__ me but

YOU DIDN'T TELL ME

Words & Music by Andrew Brown

THE GIRL I KNEW

Words & Music by Andrew Brown

1. Thought love had come my way
2. And the days we spent to-geth-er

when I saw you face to
and the end-less mov-ie

61

knew told me I could al - ways make her laugh.

Now she's liv - ing on her own,

and she's list - 'ning to sad songs. And I'm wait - ing for the

day she calls my phone and she says that she was wrong. The girl I

D.S. al Coda

64

BROKENHEARTED FT. B.o.B

Words & Music by Andrew Brown, Bobby Ray Simmons Jr.,
Ki Fitzgerald, Paddy Dalton & Mark Blackwell

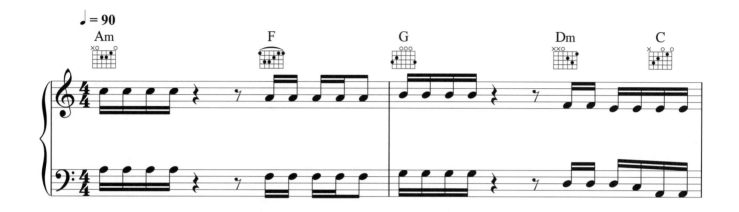

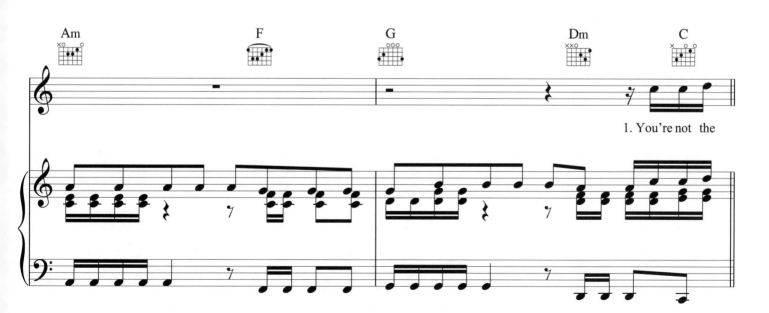

1. You're not the

JULIET

Words & Music by Carl Falk, Andrew Brown,
Eric Turner & Michel Zitron

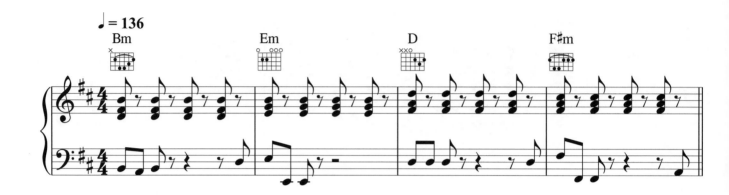

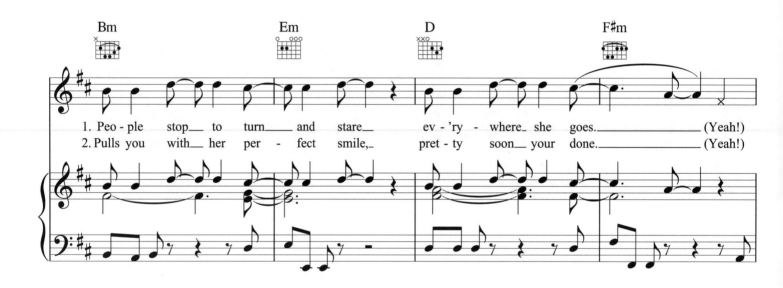

1. Peo - ple stop__ to turn__ and stare__ ev - 'ry - where__ she goes._____ (Yeah!)
2. Pulls you with__ her per - fect smile,__ pret - ty soon__ your done._____ (Yeah!)

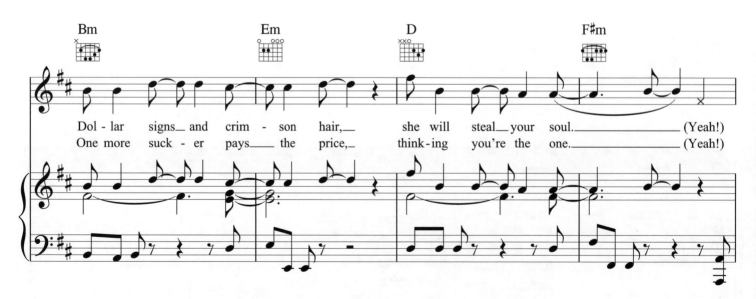

Dol - lar signs__ and crim - son hair,__ she will steal__ your soul._____ (Yeah!)
One more suck - er pays__ the price,__ think - ing you're__ the one._____ (Yeah!)

Sets her sights on bil - lion - aires, all she wants is gold. (Yeah!)
Man - y men have tried and failed, cap - tured by her gold. (Yeah!)

She is straight up rock and roll. I'm tell - in' you she knows. (Yeah!)
Stay a - way from Ju - li - et, you will lose con - trol. (Yeah!)

She know. Oh, oh, ee, oh. She know. Oh, oh, ee, oh.

No - bod - y does it like Ju - li - et. Ju - li - et, what you do to me?

LOVE LOCKED OUT

Words & Music by Andrew Brown & Matt Schwartz

me   and the way I feel.   It's a - bout to - night. Tell me
(2.) eyes,   can you feel that heat?   Can you see the glow? Tell me

please   ba - by, what's the deal?   Does he treat you right?   'Cause
please   that you want me babe,   I just got - ta know.   But

all you do is talk a - bout him and   I don't want_ to know._ 'Cause it hurts in -
all you do is talk a - bout him   time and time_ a - gain._   It hurts in -

- side   and I got no say.   And I got no say.
- side   and I got no say.   And I got no say. } He won't

77

love you like I do, ba-by. I gua-ran-tee.___ I am hap-py for you.___ Got the

guy of your dreams.___ Do we have to go through___ this ev-er-y time?___ He won't

love you like I do, I do, I do._____ That's the way you leave me,___

love locked___ out.___ That's the way you leave me,___ love locked___ out.___

ARE YOU READY?

Words & Music by Andrew Brown, Ki Fitzgerald,
Mark Blackwell & Edward Drewett

PARACHUTE

Words & Music by Andreas Carlsson, Carl Falk, Andrew Brown & Eric Turner

BACK TO LIFE

Words & Music by Gary Clark, Andrew Brown,
Harry Sommerdahl & Ki Fitzgerald

used to be._____ I don't know him. Don't know me.
-al - i - ty._____ I don't know him. Don't know me.

1° only

(Ooh, ah,_____ oh._____ Ooh, ah,_____ oh.)_____

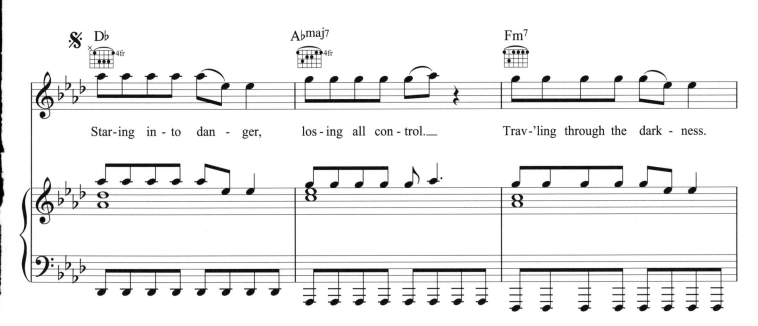

Star-ing in - to dan - ger, los - ing all con - trol.___ Trav-'ling through the dark - ness.

93